DIFFICULT LEVEL

MATCHING CHINESE CHARACTERS AND PINYIN

把汉字和拼音连起来

MANDARIN CHINESE PINYIN TEST SERIES

测试你的拼音知识

PART 17

Simplified Mandarin Chinese Characters with Pinyin and English, Mind Games, Test Your Knowledge of Pinyin with Multiple Answer Choice Puzzle Questions, Fast Reading & Vocabulary, Answers Included, Easy Lessons for Beginners, HSK All Levels

DENG YIXIN 邓艺心

ACKNOWLEDGEMENT

I would like to thank everyone who helped me complete this book, including my teachers, family members, friends, colleagues.

谢谢

Deng Yixin

邓艺心

INTRODUCTION

Chinese language and culture are a huge concept. In order to understand and appreciate Mandarin Chinese, we need to understand the language. Learning Chinese character is a very important part of learning the language. And, yes, learning pinyin is a must!

Welcome to **Connecting Chinese Characters and Pinyin Test Series**. Now you can test the knowledge of your Chinese pinyin (测试你的拼音知识). In these books and lessons therein, you will learn recognizing pinyin of the simplified Chinese characters. The books contain hundreds of character-pinyin matching **puzzles** (questions). For each question, there are Chinese characters in the left column and pinyin in the right column. You need to guess the correct pinyin of the given characters (把汉字和拼音连起来). The **English** meanings of the Chinese characters has been included a quick reference. The answers of all the question are provided at the end of the book.

CONTENTS

CHAPTER 1: QUESTIONS (1-30)

#1.

A. 宫 1. Gōng (Palace)

B. 琅 2. Láng (A surname)

C. 正 3. Zhèng (Straight)

D. 龄 4. Líng (Age)

E. 恙 5. Qiāng (An ancient axe)

F. 斨 6. Yàng (Ailment)

#2.

A. 辽 1. Xiān (Celestial being)

B. 耶 2. Liáo (Distant)

C. 参 3. Yòu (The right side)

D. 仙 4. Táo (Peach)

E. 右 5. Shēn (Ginseng)

F. 桃 6. Yé (At the end of a sentence (like 啊))

#3.

A. 枯 1. Zhūn (Grave)

B. 焚 2. Kū (Dry)

C. 龃　　3. Fén (Burn)

D. 窀　　4. Xīng (Orangutan)

E. 猩　　5. Jǔ (Irregular teeth)

F. 蠢　　6. Chǔn (Wriggle)

#4.

A. 萨　　1. Kēng (Hole)

B. 稼　　2. Tóng (Pupil of eye)

C. 奥　　3. Sà (Bodhisattva)

D. 阬　　4. Jià (Sow)

E. 旦　　5. Ào (Southwest or secret corner of house)

F. 曈　　6. Dàn (Dawn)

#5.

A. 辟　　1. Bì (The flight of steps leading to the throne hall)

B. 辗　　2. Jìn (Exhaust)

C. 陛　　3. Pì (Open up)

D. 普　　4. Pǔ (General)

E. 尽　　5. Zhēng (Male adult)

F. 丁　　6. Zhǎn (Roll)

#6.

A. 霆 1. Zào (Black)

B. 庸 2. Zā (Circumference)

C. 皂 3. Tíng (Thunder)

D. 匝 4. Yōng (Inferior)

E. 古 5. Gǔ (Antiquity)

F. 硫 6. Liú (Sulphur)

#7.

A. 粟 1. Yún (Increase)

B. 旬 2. Cī (Skeleton)

C. 员 3. Sù ()

D. 罗 4. Xún (Full period)

E. 邠 5. Luō (A net for catching birds)

F. 骴 6. Bīn (A surname)

#8.

A. 厄 1. Nì (Cover or daub with plaster, putty, etc.)

B. 泥 2. È (Strategic point)

C. 刮 3. Guā (Shave)

D. 留 4. Zǎo (Flea)

E. 朝 5. Cháo (Royal court)

F. 蚤 6. Liú (Remain)

#9.

A. 烂 1. Làn (Mashed)

B. 赣 2. Yún (Weed (the fields))

C. 耘 3. Gàn (Short name for Jiangxi province)

D. 蛇 4. Shé (Snake)

E. 鞘 5. Ēi (Hey)

F. 欸 6. Shāo (Whiplash)

#10.

A. 麻 1. Má (Hemp)

B. 死 2. Sǐ (Dead)

C. 海 3. Hǎi (Sea)

D. 娶 4. Qǔ (Marry)

E. 主 5. Shǎng (Grant a reward)

F. 赏 6. Zhǔ (Host)

#11.

A. 赊 1. Sù (Respectful)

B. 货 2. Shē (On credit)

C. 陂 3. Yú (A kind of monkey mentioned in ancient literature)

D. 禺 4. Huò (Goods)

E. 肃 5. Pí (A word used in a place name)

F. 系 6. Xì (System)

#12.

A. 笑 1. Guī (Be converted to Buddhism)

B. 凸 2. Xiào (Smile)

C. 疑 3. Xiān (Lift)

D. 皈 4. Tū (Convex)

E. 匋 5. Táo (Pottery)

F. 掀 6. Yí (Doubt)

#13.

A. 酸 1. Háo (Raccoon dog)

B. 雀 2. Shí (Lose)

C. 磐 3. Xī (The sunrise)

D. 貉 4. Pán (Big mountain stone)

E. 蚀 5. Suān (Acid)

F. 曦 6. Qiǎo (Sparrow)

#14.

A. 陡 1. Sù (Lodge for the night)

B. 靶 2. Cè (Lavatory)

C. 宿 3. Dǒu (Steep)

D. 厕 4. Huò (Perhaps)

E. 钆 5. Bǎ (Target)

F. 或 6. Gá (Gadolinium (Gd))

#15.

A. 衩 1. Shì (Test)

B. 试 2. Guǐ (Box)

C. 扉 3. Hé (Gentle)

D. 碑 4. Chǎ (Open stem of a garment)

E. 和 5. Fēi (Door panel)

F. 匦 6. Bēi (A stone tablet)

#16.

A. 匐 1. Lú (Bow of boat)

B. 彧 2. Fú (Creep)

C. 孔 3. Diǎn (Stand on tiptoe)

D. 舻 4. Yù (Elegant)

E. 秫 5. Shú (Kaoliang)

F. 踮 6. Zā (Bind)

#17.

A. 情 1. Jiàng (Stubborn)

B. 巧 2. Hán (Letter)

C. 函 3. Lí (Loriot)

D. 瘤 4. Qiǎo (Skillful)

E. 鹂 5. Liú (Tumor)

F. 强 6. Qíng (Feeling)

#18.

A. 疟 1. Tuì (Take off)

B. 黪 2. Nüè (Malaria)

C. 绥 3. Căn (Dark)

D. 畴 4. Chóu (Farmland)

E. 枯 5. Kū (Dry)

F. 褪 6. Suí (Peaceful)

#19.

A. 椭

B. 北

C. 旷

D. 袺

E. 竿

F. 懔

1. Lǐn (Austere)

2. Tuǒ (Oval)

3. Jié (Carry sth. in the front of one's jacket)

4. Běi (North)

5. Gān (Pole)

6. Kuàng (Vast)

#20.

A. 焚

B. 糕

C. 亨

D. 鳔

E. 狐

F. 韩

1. Biào (Swim bladder of fish)

2. Fén (Burn)

3. Hú (Fox)

4. Gāo (Cake)

5. Hēng (Prosperous)

6. Hán (South Korea)

#21.

A. 洌

B. 稚

C. 礼

D. 醌

E. 辽

1. Lǐ (Courtesy)

2. Liú (Sulphur)

3. Liáo (Distant)

4. Kūn (Quinone)

5. Liè (Crystal-clear)

F. 硫 6. Zhì (Young)

#22.

A. 甙 1. Dài (Glucoside)

B. 细 2. Piān (Small)

C. 怔 3. Gān (Swill)

D. 泔 4. Xì (Fine)

E. 扁 5. Mì (Secrete)

F. 泌 6. Zhèng (Stare blankly)

#23.

A. 勺 1. Jū (Jade pendant)

B. 齐 2. Sháo (Spoon)

C. 琚 3. Qí (Neat)

D. 舨 4. Yīng (Should)

E. 应 5. Méng (Ridge of a roof)

F. 甍 6. Bǎn (Small boat)

#24.

A. 后 1. Hòu (Rear)

B. 监 2. Cǎi (Pick)

C. 沃 3. Fěi (Be at a loss for words)

D. 中 4. Wò (To water)

E. 采 5. Jiàn (An imperial office)

F. 悱 6. Zhōng (Centre)

#25.

A. 公 1. Què (Crack)

B. 隼 2. Gōng (State-owned)

C. 丫 3. Gōng (Attack)

D. 郤 4. Yā (Ah)

E. 攻 5. Tǎn (A kind of jade)

F. 璮 6. Sǔn (Falcon)

#26.

A. 迅 1. Tuǐ (Leg)

B. 弃 2. Dìng (Calm)

C. 盛 3. Jǔ (Collect)

D. 定 4. Chéng (Fill)

E. 虓 5. Xiāo (Tiger's angry roar)

F. 腿 6. Xùn (Fast)

#27.

A. 九 | 1. Bèi (A wolf-like animal with short forelegs)
B. 既 | 2. Jì (Already)
C. 馃 | 3. Guǒ (Cake)
D. 本 | 4. Qīng (Incline)
E. 狈 | 5. Běn (Stem or root of plants)
F. 倾 | 6. Jiǔ (Nine)

#28.

A. 馔 | 1. Jié (Clean)
B. 牵 | 2. Fàn (Farmland, often used in place names)
C. 厉 | 3. Lì (Stern)
D. 絜 | 4. Fú (Undercurrent)
E. 畈 | 5. Zhuàn (Food)
F. 洑 | 6. Qiān (Lead)

#29.

A. 蜇 | 1. Bìng (Illness)
B. 晕 | 2. Zhē (Bite)
C. 病 | 3. Shā (Sand)
D. 沙 | 4. Yūn (Dizzy)

E. 晨　　　　5. Chén (Morning)

F. 龄　　　　6. Líng (Age)

#30.

A. 剥　　　　1. Xī (Warm)

B. 教　　　　2. Nài (A kind of apple)

C. 熹　　　　3. Zhān (Glue)

D. 漂　　　　4. Piào (Fai)

E. 柰　　　　5. Bāo (Skin)

F. 粘　　　　6. Jiào (Religion)

CHAPTER 2: QUESTIONS (31-60)

#31.

A. 尾 | 1. Shàn (Support)
B. 赡 | 2. Jiàng (Craftsman)
C. 改 | 3. Wěi (Tail)
D. 飞 | 4. Fēi (Fly)
E. 骷 | 5. Kū (Skull without skin or hair)
F. 匠 | 6. Gǎi (Change)

#32.

A. 弎 | 1. Guì (Kneel)
B. 设 | 2. Dàng (Proper)
C. 当 | 3. Dǔ (Stop up)
D. 跪 | 4. Kuài (Piece)
E. 块 | 5. Sān (Variant of 三)
F. 堵 | 6. Shè (Set up)

#33.

A. 飙 | 1. Liú (Sulphur)
B. 陉 | 2. Xíng (Break in a mountain ridge)

C. 硫 3. Ròu (Meat)

D. 肝 4. Biāo (Storm)

E. 初 5. Chū (For the first time)

F. 肉 6. Gān (Liver)

#34.

A. 丹 1. Ào (A surname)

B. 浇 2. Liú (Remain)

C. 留 3. Dān (Ref)

D. 欺 4. Huái (Bosom)

E. 耷 5. Qī (Deceive)

F. 怀 6. Dā (Ears hanging down)

#35.

A. 齐 1. Kē (Nest)

B. 窠 2. Sǔn (Bamboo shoot)

C. 靬 3. Qì (Throw away)

D. 弃 4. Jué (Discontented)

E. 笋 5. Jì (Flavoring)

F. 觖 6. Qián (In place names)

#36.

A. 宿 1. Sù (Lodge for the night)

B. 台 2. Tái (Tower)

C. 聆 3. Huī (Tease)

D. 览 4. Líng (Hear)

E. 诙 5. Lǎn (Take a look at)

F. 髋 6. Kuān (Hip)

#37.

A. 烦 1. Yù (Then)

B. 龋 2. Qǔ (Bad teeth)

C. 聿 3. Kuí (Surname)

D. 弑 4. Xiào (Smile)

E. 奎 5. Fán (Trouble)

F. 笑 6. Shì (Murder)

#38.

A. 虒 1. Nú (Inferior horse)

B. 艖 2. Zhōu (Congee)

C. 驽 3. Suǒ (Cable)

D. 赩 4. Xì (Red)

E. 粥 5. Chā (Small boat)

F. 索 6. Sī (A legendary beast)

#39.

A. 袎 1. Qí (Strange)

B. 列 2. Yào (Leg of a boot)

C. 酶 3. Róu (Mix)

D. 糅 4. Liè (Arrange)

E. 兹 5. Méi (Enzyme)

F. 觭 6. Zī (This)

#40.

A. 揣 1. Chuāi (Hide things in one's clothes)

B. 洎 2. Nüè (Cruel)

C. 虐 3. Yáo (Meat and fish dishes)

D. 阮 4. Ruǎn (Nephew)

E. 肴 5. Xùn (Flood)

F. 汛 6. Jì (Reach (a point or a period of time))

#41.

A. 罛 1. Jià (Harness)

B. 驾　　2. Mì (River name in Mìluó)

C. 富　　3. Gū (Large fishing nets)

D. 盟　　4. Fù (Rich)

E. 汨　　5. Jiù (Vulture)

F. 鹫　　6. Míng (Swear)

#42.

A. 瓷　　1. Guān (Huge fish)

B. 黪　　2. Píng (A surname)

C. 童　　3. Căn (Dark)

D. 鳏　　4. Tè (Disturbed)

E. 忑　　5. Tóng (Child)

F. 邢　　6. Cí (Porcelain)

#43.

A. 合　　1. Yìn (Give water to drink)

B. 耜　　2. Sì (A spade-shaped farm tool used in ancient China)

C. 饮　　3. Xún (Ten days)

D. 罟　　4. Gŭ (Fish net)

E. 艮　　5. Gě (Ge, a unit of dry measure for grain)

F. 旬　　6. Gěn (Blunt)

#44.

A. 酶 1. Méi (Enzyme)

B. 梵 2. Fàn (Buddhist)

C. 曝 3. Tuó (A small bay in a river)

D. 产 4. Chǎn (Give birth to)

E. 沱 5. Pù (Expose to the sun)

F. 瓶 6. Píng (Bottle)

#45.

A. 骂 1. Rèn (Appoint)

B. 郦 2. Mà (Curse)

C. 旒 3. Liú (Tassel)

D. 胤 4. Sǎn (Umbrella)

E. 任 5. Yìn (Offspring)

F. 伞 6. Lì (A surname)

#46.

A. 死 1. Chéng (Sincere)

B. 幺 2. Yāo (One (used for the numeral orally))

C. 殂 3. Sǐ (Dead)

D. 肄 4. Fěi (Rich with literary grace)

E. 诚 5. Cú (Die)

F. 斐 6. Yì (Study)

#47.

A. 奚 1. Sōu (Great boat)

B. 艘 2. Xī (What)

C. 颜 3. Yán (Face)

D. 丢 4. Xī (Selenium)

E. 郊 5. Jiāo (Suburbs)

F. 硒 6. Diū (Lose)

#48.

A. 北 1. Xiáo (Confuse)

B. 弱 2. Běi (North)

C. 晶 3. Jīng (Crystal)

D. 殽 4. Qiáng (Strong)

E. 强 5. Jià (Price)

F. 价 6. Ruò (Weak)

#49.

A. 炸 1. Hún (Soul)

B. 霹 2. Zhà (Explode)

C. 邙 3. Máng (The name of the mountain, in Henan Province, China)

D. 解 4. Jiè (Send under guard)

E. 魂 5. Zhēng (The first moon)

F. 正 6. Wèi (Rising)

#50.

A. 踯 1. Fàn (Farmland, often used in place names)

B. 遁 2. Hù (A kind of edible gourd)

C. 饴 3. Yí (Maltose)

D. 魂 4. Dùn (Escape)

E. 畈 5. Hún (Soul)

F. 瓠 6. Zhí (Pace up and down)

#51.

A. 髑 1. Yú (A kind of monkey mentioned in ancient literature)

B. 趟 2. Tāng (Ford)

C. 禺 3. Kū (Skull without skin or hair)

D. 对 4. Gǒu (Chinese wolfberry)

E. 栒 5. Duì (Answer)

F. 骷 6. Qǔ (Bad teeth)

#52.

A. 耤 1. Shà (A tall building)

B. 晟 2. Áo (Boil)

C. 熬 3. Bā (Cake)

D. 豺 4. Chái (Jackal)

E. 厦 5. Shèng (Bright)

F. 粑 6. Jí (Plough)

#53.

A. 允 1. Chú (Get rid of)

B. 弁 2. Yǔn (Allow)

C. 曼 3. Màn (Graceful)

D. 骺 4. Jì (Tie)

E. 系 5. Hóu (Epiphysis)

F. 除 6. Biàn (A man's cap used in ancient times)

#54.

A. 踏 1. Zhú (Stern of a ship)

B. 舳 2. Tà (Step on)

C. 耐 3. Nài (Be able to bear)

D. 分 4. Fēn (Divide)

E. 站 5. Jì (Crucian carp)

F. 鲫 6. Zhàn (Stand)

#55.

A. 掣 1. Qiú (Chief of a tribe)

B. 瓴 2. Líng (Water jar)

C. 繇 3. Yóu (By means of)

D. 酋 4. Chè (Pull)

E. 幽 5. Gū (Mushroom)

F. 菇 6. Yōu (Quiet)

#56.

A. 印 1. Yìn (Seal)

B. 渣 2. Chǎo (Stir-fry)

C. 笼 3. Sān (Three)

D. 叁 4. Lǒng (Cover)

E. 炒 5. Wú (Centipede)

F. 蜈 6. Zhā (Dregs)

#57.

A. 划　　1. Rù (Elaborate)

B. 博　　2. Bó (Rich)

C. 将　　3. Huà (Delimit)

D. 舰　　4. Shēng (Sound)

E. 声　　5. Jiāng (Support)

F. 缛　　6. Jiàn (Warship)

#58.

A. 蛤　　1. Tài (Discard)

B. 汰　　2. Jì (Reach (a point or a period of time))

C. 烧　　3. Lòu (Reveal)

D. 旆　　4. gé (Clams)

E. 洎　　5. Shāo (Burn)

F. 露　　6. Pèi (Flag)

#59.

A. 酬　　1. Zhēng (A legendary leopard-like beast)

B. 瘸　　2. Qué (Be lame)

C. 鲊　　3. Zhǎ (Salted fish)

D. 狰 4. Duò (Fall)

E. 彤 5. Chóu (Propose a toast)

F. 堕 6. Tóng (Red)

#60.

A. 科 1. Qiān (Kilowatt)

B. 那 2. Jiǒng (In straitened circumstances)

C. 瓩 3. Liáng (Grain)

D. 粮 4. Nà (That)

E. 窘 5. Kē (A branch of academic or vocational study)

F. 疙 6. Gē (Wart)

CHAPTER 3: QUESTIONS (61-90)

#61.

A. 克 1. Má (Hemp)

B. 从 2. Dàng (Pool)

C. 沦 3. Huǎng (Dazzle)

D. 氹 4. Cóng (From)

E. 晃 5. Lún (Sink)

F. 麻 6. Kè (Gram (g))

#62.

A. 辜 1. Yùn (Halo)

B. 阶 2. Xiù (Put forth flowers or ears)

C. 猢 3. Hú (Primates, especially the macaques from northern China)

D. 晕 4. Gū (Gu (surname))

E. 瓯 5. Ōu (Bowl)

F. 秀 6. Jiē (Steps)

#63.

A. 觉 1. Cù (Kick)

B. 翡 2. Tā (Collapse)

C. 蹴 3. Fěi (Kingfisher)

D. 辟 4. Jiào (Sleep)

E. 塌 5. Dīng (Mend the sole of a shoe)

F. 靪 6. Bì (Monarch)

#64.

A. 踢 1. Jiàng (Stubborn)

B. 痕 2. Yì (Name of a master archer)

C. 縻 3. Hén (Mark)

D. 羿 4. Tī (To kick)

E. 罔 5. Mí (Harness)

F. 强 6. Wǎng (Deceive)

#65.

A. 坊 1. Shè (Shoot)

B. 轧 2. Xī (A surname)

C. 郗 3. Fáng (Workshop)

D. 颤 4. Nián (Sticky)

E. 射 5. Zhá (Roll)

F. 粘 6. Chàn (Quiver)

#66.

A. 耎 1. Tán (Deep)

B. 试 2. Zhuàn (Revolve)

C. 转 3. Sì (Nasal mucus)

D. 豫 4. Shì (Test)

E. 覃 5. Ruǎn (Weak)

F. 泗 6. Yù (Live in ease and comfort)

#67.

A. 狗 1. Jū (Reside)

B. 曦 2. Shèng (Bright)

C. 居 3. Gǔ (Antiquity)

D. 晟 4. Xī (The sunrise)

E. 古 5. Gǒu (Dog)

F. 於 6. Wū (What)

#68.

A. 秃 1. Guǎ (Cut into pieces)

B. 剐 2. Tū (Bald)

C. 乢 3. Ěr (You)

D. 尔 4. Tíng (The court of a feudal ruler)

E. 支 5. Zhī (Support)

F. 廷 6. Qié (Chinese yam)

#69.

A. 粒 1. Qióng (Vault)

B. 北 2. Běi (North)

C. 髁 3. Kē (Condyle)

D. 丁 4. Zhēng (Male adult)

E. 穹 5. Lì (Small particles)

F. 辣 6. Là (Peppery)

#70.

A. 来 1. Táo (Pottery)

B. 匋 2. Huī (Clamor)

C. 欣 3. Cè (Survey)

D. 豗 4. Diăn (Drop)

E. 点 5. Lái (Come)

F. 测 6. Xīn (Glad)

#71.

A. 卡 1. Qiă (Wedge)

B. 坊 2. Dōng (Winter)

C. 冬 3. Kěn (Cultivate)

D. 搂 4. Lǒu (Hug)

E. 垦 5. Bēi (A stone tablet)

F. 碑 6. Fáng (Workshop)

#72.

A. 售 1. Shòu (Sell)

B. 嚏 2. Wǎn (As if)

C. 重 3. Tì (Sneeze)

D. 吓 4. Hè (Threaten)

E. 宛 5. Yīng (Eagle)

F. 鹰 6. Zhòng (Weight)

#73.

A. 空 1. Yǐ (Ochre)

B. 舣 2. Xíng (Form)

C. 劣 3. Liè (Bad)

D. 缳 4. Huá (Paddle)

E. 形 5. Huán (Tie around with ropes)

F. 划 6. Kòng (Leave empty or blank)

#74.

A. 雯 1. Tè (Disturbed)

B. 徯 2. Mì (Secret)

C. 审 3. Shěn (Careful)

D. 密 4. Guà (Hang)

E. 忑 5. Wén (Cloud in beautiful patterns)

F. 挂 6. Xī (To quarrel)

#75.

A. 罭 1. Xiè (Crab)

B. 龃 2. Tè (Particular)

C. 之 3. Jǔ (Irregular teeth)

D. 特 4. Piāo (Float)

E. 蟹 5. Yù (Dragnet)

F. 飘 6. Zhī (This)

#76.

A. 剐 1. Miè (Thin bamboo strip)

B. 伪 2. Yān (Here)

C. 篾 3. Nì (Cover or daub with plaster, putty, etc.)

D. 焉 4. Guǎ (Cut into pieces)

E. 泥 5. Wěi (Pseudo)

F. 窈 6. Yǎo (Deep)

#77.

A. 济 1. Zhì (Young)

B. 翊 2. Yé (Grandfather)

C. 排 3. Zhēng (Seized with terror)

D. 爷 4. Pái (Row)

E. 稚 5. Yì (Assist (a ruler))

F. 怔 6. Jì (Cross a river)

#78.

A. 尚 1. Fén (Burn)

B. 瘟 2. Wēn (Acute communicable diseases)

C. 恢 3. Shàng (Still)

D. 飘 4. Yáo (Drifting with the wind)

E. 丢 5. Huī (Extensive)

F. 焚 6. Diū (Lose)

#79.

A. 戗　　1. Hóng (Rainbow)

B. 虹　　2. Xīn (Salary)

C. 逯　　3. Lù (Jade-like stone)

D. 捡　　4. Capture (Catch)

E. 褟　　5. Tā (Undershirt)

F. 薪　　6. Qiàng (Prop)

#80.

A. 廷　　1. Nì (Close)

B. 窘　　2. Nòng (Do)

C. 沿　　3. Tíng (The court of a feudal ruler)

D. 昵　　4. Yàn (Water's edge)

E. 弄　　5. Jiǒng (In straitened circumstances)

F. 牧　　6. Mù (Herd)

#81.

A. 瞑　　1. Yù (A surname)

B. 历　　2. Má (Hemp)

C. 居　　3. Lì (Experience)

D. 尉　　4. Jū (Reside)

E. 乳　　5. Rǔ (Give birth to)

F. 麻 6. Míng (Close the eyes)

#82.

A. 纫 1. Rèn (Thread)

B. 廓 2. Méng (Sprout)

C. 萌 3. Yě (And also)

D. 炸 4. Zhá (Fry in deep fat or oil)

E. 羡 5. Kuò (Outline)

F. 也 6. Xiàn (Admire)

#83.

A. 歼 1. Jué (The rank of nobility)

B. 鳊 2. Jiān (Annihilate)

C. 背 3. Nà (Patch up)

D. 爵 4. Gé (Arrowroot)

E. 葛 5. Bèi (Body's back)

F. 衲 6. Biān (Bream)

#84.

A. 阵 1. Lú (Bow of boat)

B. 餍 2. Xún (Look for)

C. 寻 3. Bā (Scar)

D. 疤 4. Xū (Need)

E. 需 5. Zhèn (Battle array)

F. 舮 6. Shèn (Clams)

#85.

A. 转 1. Liáo (Distant)

B. 辽 2. Dài (Take the place of)

C. 古 3. Zhuàn (Revolve)

D. 文 4. Wén (Character)

E. 代 5. Gǔ (Antiquity)

F. 轮 6. Lún (Wheel)

#86.

A. 惹 1. Máng (Chinese silver grass)

B. 芒 2. Rě (Provoke)

C. 蒜 3. Suàn (Garlic)

D. 旧 4. Hū (Breathe out)

E. 沸 5. Jiù (Past)

F. 呼 6. Fèi (Boil)

#87.

A. 匹 1. Yā (Duck)

B. 圾 2. Pǐ (Be equal to)

C. 炉 3. Lú (Stove)

D. 弯 4. Jìshēng (Garbage)

E. 寿 5. Shòu (Longevity)

F. 鸭 6. Wān (Curved)

#88.

A. 的 1. Zhàn (Occupy)

B. 汪 2. Dí (Taxi)

C. 烹 3. Dèng (Deng, a state in the Zhou Dynasty)

D. 邓 4. Wāng (A surname)

E. 占 5. Bǎn (Board)

F. 板 6. Pēng (Boil)

#89.

A. 网 1. Bāo (Wrap)

B. 旖 2. Lián (Flag on pole over wine house)

C. 届 3. Yàn (Used in place names)

D. 匽 4. Yǐ (The appearance of the flags fluttering in the wind)

E. 帘 5. Jiè (Fall due)

F. 包 6. Wǎng (Network)

#90.

A. 骴 1. Cī (Skeleton)

B. 咸 2. Cǐ (Clear)

C. 野 3. Yě (Open country)

D. 泚 4. Xián (All)

E. 硅 5. Guī (Silicon)

F. 馇 6. Chā (Cook and stir)

CHAPTER 4: QUESTIONS (91-120)

#91.

A. 昪 1. Biàn (Bright)

B. 瓩 2. Xún (Look for)

C. 郪 3. Qī (A surname)

D. 北 4. Běi (North)

E. 寻 5. Qiān (Kilowatt)

F. 搭 6. Dā (Build)

#92.

A. 酸 1. Bāo (Afterbirth)

B. 糟 2. Suān (Acid)

C. 蛋 3. Mǐn (Perish)

D. 瓻 4. Chī (Wine pot)

E. 胞 5. Zāo (Dregs)

F. 泯 6. Dàn (Egg)

#93.

A. 艖 1. Dǒu (Steep)

B. 祭 2. Dàn (Egg)

C. 蛋 3. Chā (Small boat)

D. 陡 4. Jié (Outstanding person)

E. 杰 5. Jì (Hold a memorial ceremony for)

F. 耆 6. Qí (Very old)

#94.

A. 冈 1. Jiào (Cellar or pit for storing things)

B. 窖 2. Gāng (Ridge (of a hill))

C. 惚 3. Yā (Pressure)

D. 豮 4. Fén (Male livestock)

E. 亨 5. Hēng (Prosperous)

F. 压 6. Hū (Dim)

#95.

A. 戚 1. Xī (Exclamatory particle)

B. 兮 2. Qiǎ (Wedge)

C. 觑 3. Hàng (A vast expanse of water)

D. 浆 4. Qī (Relative)

E. 卡 5. Qū (Narrow)

F. 沆 6. Jiāng (Thick liquid)

#96.

A. 戒 1. Jiàng (Stubborn)

B. 彬 2. Jiè (Guard against)

C. 强 3. Bīn (Fine)

D. 板 4. Din (Indigo)

E. 靛 5. Bǎn (Board)

F. 翅 6. Chì (Wing)

#97.

A. 汽 1. Què (Step back)

B. 但 2. Dàn (Only)

C. 尉 3. Liào ((Of a draught animal) kick backward with its hind legs)

D. 尥 4. Qì (Vapor)

E. 却 5. Gāo (Cake)

F. 糕 6. Yù (A surname)

#98.

A. 穸 1. Xī (Night)

B. 相 2. Méi (Plum)

C. 梅 3. Luǎn (Egg)

D. 旁 4. Páng (Other)

E. 卵 5. Xiāng (Each other)

F. 关 6. Guān (Turn off)

#99.

A. 航 1. Qióng (Poor)

B. 孰 2. Bì (Avoid)

C. 隋 3. Bàn (Mix)

D. 避 4. Shú (What)

E. 穷 5. Háng (Boat)

F. 拌 6. Suí (The Sui Dynasty)

#100.

A. 厌 1. Niáng (Ma)

B. 酋 2. Shì (Posthumous title)

C. 昼 3. Zhòu (Daytime)

D. 舿 4. Yàn (Be satisfied)

E. 谥 5. Jī (Odd)

F. 娘 6. Qiú (Chief of a tribe)

#101.

A. 猋　　1. Dān (A word used in a person's name)

B. 串　　2. Chuàn (String together)

C. 费　　3. Fèi (Fee)

D. 魑　　4. Qī (Deceive)

E. 聃　　5. Biāo (Dashing)

F. 欺　　6. Chī (Demons)

#102.

A. 秦　　1. Lián (Unite)

B. 匿　　2. Qín (The Qin Dynasty)

C. 坐　　3. Zuò (Sit)

D. 奘　　4. Zhuǎng (Big and thick)

E. 联　　5. Fàn (Farmland, often used in place names)

F. 畈　　6. Nì (Hide)

#103.

A. 古　　1. Shǐ (Excrement)

B. 疗　　2. Gǔ (Antiquity)

C. 篇　　3. Piān (A piece of writing)

D. 罥　　4. Juàn (Bird catching net)

E. 浇　　5. Jiāo (Pour liquid on)

F. 屎　　6. Liáo (Cure)

#104.

A. 非　　1. Kuí (A one-legged monster in the fables)

B. 餮　　2. Tiè (Gluttonous)

C. 购　　3. Jiào (Religion)

D. 魅　　4. Mèi (Goblin)

E. 夔　　5. Gòu (Purchase)

F. 教　　6. Fēi (Un-)

#105.

A. 午　　1. Shì (Murder)

B. 鸵　　2. Tuó (Ostrich)

C. 弑　　3. Bó (Rich)

D. 博　　4. Wǔ (Noon)

E. 燃　　5. Pǎng (Thigh)

F. 髈　　6. Rán (Burn)

#106.

A. 它　　1. Yǔ (Give)

B. 即　　2. Wā (Dig)

C. 酱　　　3. Jí (Which is)

D. 量　　　4. Tā (It)

E. 挖　　　5. Jiàng (Paste)

F. 予　　　6. Liáng (Measure)

#107.

A. 裱　　　1. Cè (Lavatory)

B. 雅　　　2. Yǎ (Refined)

C. 厕　　　3. Zhèn (Sign)

D. 朕　　　4. Yūn (Dizzy)

E. 晕　　　5. Biǎo (Mounting)

F. 椭　　　6. Tuǒ (Oval)

#108.

A. 勒　　　1. Dǒu (Steep)

B. 付　　　2. Lè (Rein in)

C. 眛　　　3. Yù (A surname)

D. 陡　　　4. Fù (Pay)

E. 凋　　　5. Diāo (Withered)

F. 尉　　　6. Mò (Light white)

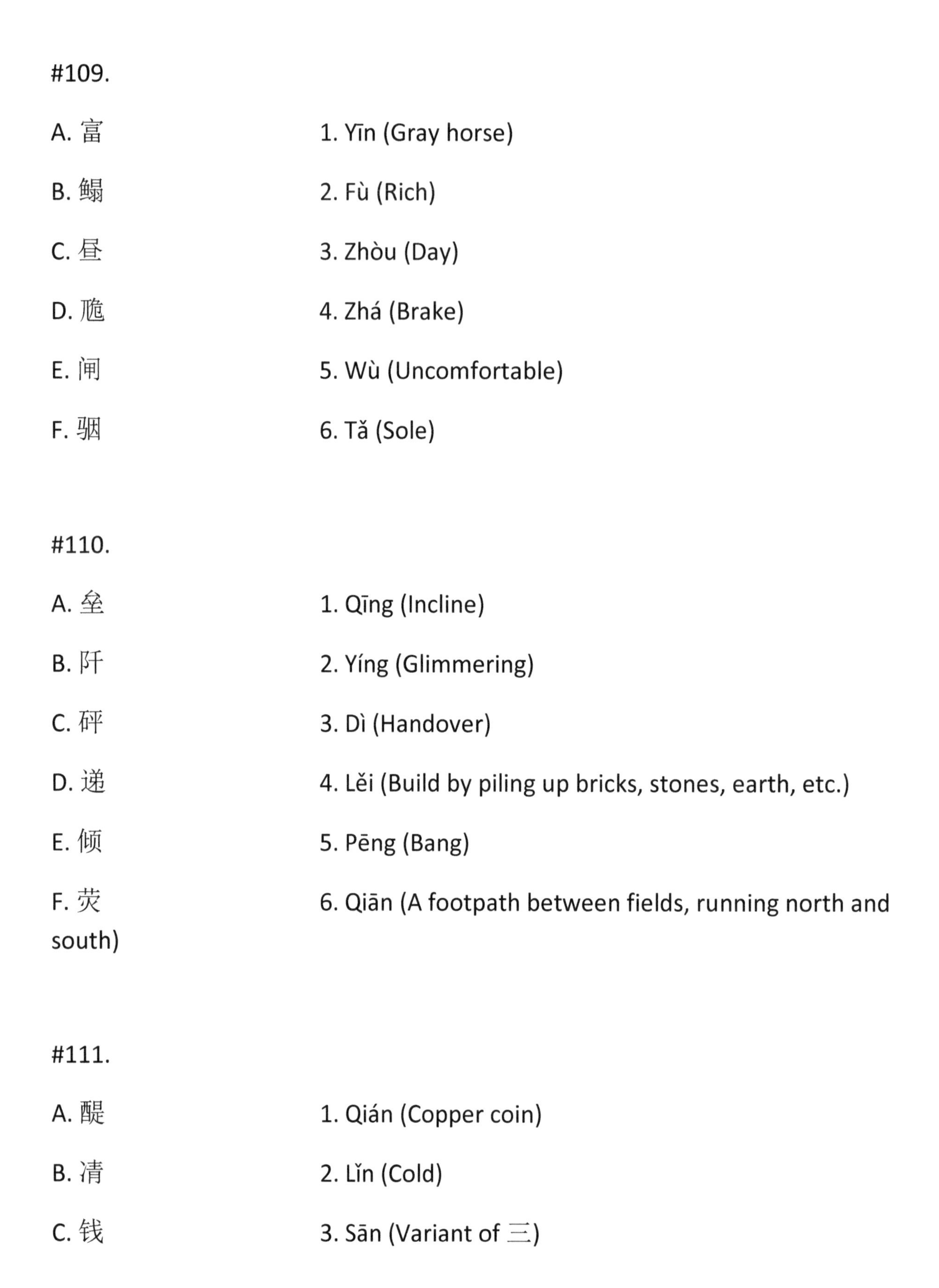

#109.

A. 富　　1. Yīn (Gray horse)

B. 鳎　　2. Fù (Rich)

C. 昼　　3. Zhòu (Day)

D. 尯　　4. Zhá (Brake)

E. 闸　　5. Wù (Uncomfortable)

F. 骃　　6. Tǎ (Sole)

#110.

A. 垒　　1. Qīng (Incline)

B. 阡　　2. Yíng (Glimmering)

C. 砰　　3. Dì (Handover)

D. 递　　4. Lěi (Build by piling up bricks, stones, earth, etc.)

E. 倾　　5. Pēng (Bang)

F. 荧　　6. Qiān (A footpath between fields, running north and south)

#111.

A. 醍　　1. Qián (Copper coin)

B. 凊　　2. Lǐn (Cold)

C. 钱　　3. Sān (Variant of 三)

D. 逻		4. Qìng (Chilly)

E. 凛		5. Luó (Patrol)

F. 貳		6. Tí (Red wine)

#112.

A. 辗		1. Pó (A surname)

B. 净		2. Tīng (A word used in a place name)

C. 划		3. Huà (Delimit)

D. 和		4. Jìng (Clean)

E. 繁		5. Hé (Gentle)

F. 町		6. Zhǎn (Roll)

#113.

A. 貅		1. Fú (Creep)

B. 处		2. Xīng (Orangutan)

C. 窿		3. Xiū (Fabulous wild beast)

D. 匐		4. Lóng (Gallery)

E. 弌		5. Chù (Place)

F. 猩		6. Yī (One)

#114.

A. 亨 1. Mí (A type of monkey)

B. 厄 2. Hēng (Prosperous)

C. 猕 3. Huī (Ash)

D. 廷 4. Xū (Dark)

E. 魆 5. È (Strategic point)

F. 灰 6. Tíng (The court of a feudal ruler)

#115.

A. 施 1. Jìn (Exhaust)

B. 净 2. Jìng (Clean)

C. 汾 3. Hěn (Ruthless)

D. 尽 4. Shī (Execute)

E. 昆 5. Kūn (Elder brother)

F. 狠 6. Fén (The name of a river in Shanxi Province)

#116.

A. 褪 1. Ēi (Hey)

B. 叛 2. Tùn (Slip out of sth)

C. 索 3. Lì (Scold)

D. 詈 4. Qiān (Thousand)

E. 千 5. Pàn (Betray)

F. 索

6. Suǒ (Cable)

#117.

A. 怖

1. Lǐ (Courtesy)

B. 叁

2. Bù (Be afraid of)

C. 笃

3. Dǔ (Sincere)

D. 礼

4. Sān (Three)

E. 夭

5. Yāo (Tender)

F. 曌

6. Zhào (The name Wu Zetian)

#118.

A. 骸

1. Hái (Body)

B. 罦

2. Jià (Price)

C. 罝

3. Jū (Net for catching hare)

D. 价

4. Xù (A surname)

E. 巷

5. Fú (Bird-net)

F. 浒

6. Xiàng (Lane)

#119.

A. 瑞

1. Ruì (Auspicious)

B. 赵

2. Zhì (Remember)

C. 褴　　3. Yùn (A surname)

D. 鲌　　4. Zhào (Zhao, a state in the Zhou Dynasty)

E. 郓　　5. Bà (Spanish mackerel)

F. 识　　6. Lán (Ragged garments)

#120.

A. 沿　　1. Jiào (Cellar or pit for storing things)

B. 觊　　2. Jì (Attempt)

C. 窖　　3. Tuó (Ostrich)

D. 夒　　4. Yán (Along)

E. 鸵　　5. Xìng (Mood or desire to do sth)

F. 兴　　6. Náo (A kind of gibbon)

CHAPTER 5: QUESTIONS (121-150)

#121.

A. 艒 1. Cuō (White spirit)

B. 泼 2. Nà (Patch up)

C. 醝 3. Áo (Stroll)

D. 衲 4. Mù (Boat)

E. 弱 5. Ruò (Weak)

F. 敖 6. Pō (Sprinkle)

#122.

A. 弈 1. Nòu (Weeding hoe)

B. 笔 2. Yàn (Water's edge)

C. 沿 3. Yì (Play chess)

D. 耨 4. Bǐ (Pen)

E. 禀 5. Zuǒ (The left side)

F. 左 6. Bǐng (Report)

#123.

A. 霜 1. Shāo (A little)

B. 欹 2. Bǐng (Report)

C. 魆 3. Jù (Straw sandals)

D. 屦 4. Qī (Lean to one side)

E. 禀 5. Shuāng (Horse)

F. 稍 6. Xū (Dark)

#124.

A. 场 1. Fēi (Mistake)

B. 觉 2. Lán (Bright-colored)

C. 毕 3. Cháng (A level open space)

D. 李 4. Lǐ (Plum)

E. 非 5. Bì (Finish)

F. 斓 6. Jué (Feel)

#125.

A. 黠 1. Lǔ (Captive)

B. 贷 2. Dí (Bamboo flute)

C. 笛 3. Jūn (Armed forces)

D. 虏 4. Dài (Loan)

E. 量 5. Liàng (Measure)

F. 军 6. Xiá (Crafty)

#126.

A. 再 1. Tóng (Same)

B. 袆 2. Zài (Again)

C. 禁 3. Huī (A pheasant pattern on the clothes)

D. 同 4. Zhōu (Congee)

E. 粥 5. Míng (Swear)

F. 盟 6. Jīn (Bear)

#127.

A. 贰 1. Mì (Secrete)

B. 聊 2. Sì (Wanton)

C. 泌 3. Miù (Pretend)

D. 肆 4. Mó (Rub)

E. 摩 5. Liáo (Merely)

F. 缪 6. Èr (Two)

#128.

A. 泊 1. Rèn (Thread)

B. 龁 2. Hé (To bite)

C. 纫 3. Fù (Fragrance)

D. 冉 4. Cū (Wide)

E. 馥 5. Rǎn (Edge of tortoise-shell)

F. 粗 6. Pō (Lake)

#129.

A. 宕 1. Gū (Mushroom)

B. 汧 2. Zài (Exist)

C. 在 3. Xuàn (Jade)

D. 菇 4. Dàng (Cave dwelling)

E. 猜 5. Qiān ()

F. 琄 6. Cāi (Guess)

#130.

A. 枸 1. Táng (For nothing)

B. 璮 2. Tǎn (A kind of jade)

C. 腚 3. Huī (Clamor)

D. 元 4. Yuán (First)

E. 唐 5. Dìng (Buttocks)

F. 豗 6. Gǒu (Chinese wolfberry)

#131.

A. 翔 1. Xiáng (Circle in the air)

B. 觞　　2. Dàng (Water puddle)

C. 凼　　3. Shāng (Wine cup)

D. 主　　4. Zhǔ (Host)

E. 好　　5. Lóu (An animal-drawn seed plough)

F. 耧　　6. Hǎo (Good)

#132.

A. 繇　　1. Zhēng (The first moon)

B. 螽　　2. Zhōng (General name for grasshoppers and crickets)

C. 邮　　3. Kuài (A surname)

D. 正　　4. Yóu (Post)

E. 郐　　5. Yáo (Slave)

F. 挐　　6. Rú (A surname)

#133.

A. 廉　　1. Shú (What)

B. 孰　　2. Yā (Ah)

C. 珽　　3. Tǐng (Scepter)

D. 兰　　4. Zhēn (Discriminate)

E. 甄　　5. Lián (Inexpensive)

F. 丫　　6. Lán (Orchid)

#134.

A. 尽　　　1. Nǎo (Brain)

B. 歪　　　2. Jiàn (Cheap)

C. 奘　　　3. Lún (Order)

D. 贱　　　4. Zhuǎng (Big and thick)

E. 伦　　　5. Jǐn (To the greatest extent)

F. 脑　　　6. Wāi (Askew)

#135.

A. 视　　　1. Ruǎn (Opaque)

B. 颤　　　2. Zhàn (Shiver)

C. 解　　　3. Xiè (Understand)

D. 瓀　　　4. Dàn (Egg)

E. 蛋　　　5. Shì (Look at)

F. 会　　　6. Huì (Get together)

#136.

A. 要　　　1. Yāo (Demand)

B. 敌　　　2. Dí (Enemy)

C. 谦　　　3. Yāng (Mandarin duck)

D. 临 4. Qiān (Modest)

E. 爸 5. Bà (Pa)

F. 谦 6. Lín (Be close to)

#137.

A. 郎 1. Lún (Wheel)

B. 考 2. Shǔ (Category)

C. 赋 3. Fù (Endow)

D. 属 4. Náng (A kind of crusty pancake)

E. 轮 5. Láng (An ancient official title)

F. 馕 6. Kǎo (Test)

#138.

A. 滑 1. Biān (Bats)

B. 箱 2. Shè (Set up)

C. 髁 3. Xiāng (Chest)

D. 隼 4. Sǔn (Falcon)

E. 设 5. Kē (Condyle)

F. 蝙 6. Huá (Slip)

#139.

A. 邵 1. Kè (Gram (g))

B. 瘟 2. Qiě (Just)

C. 克 3. Wēn (Acute communicable diseases)

D. 且 4. Shǐ (Excrement)

E. 屎 5. Juān (Cuckoo)

F. 鹃 6. Shào (Excellent)

#140.

A. 沾 1. Jiāng (Ginger)

B. 霉 2. Tī (To kick)

C. 房 3. Zhān (Wet)

D. 愐 4. Fáng (House)

E. 姜 5. Méi (Mold)

F. 踢 6. Miǎn (Diligence)

#141.

A. 膏 1. Zhé (A wise and intelligent person)

B. 鲑 2. Gāo (Fat)

C. 盟 3. Xiè (The legendary god sheep)

D. 喆 4. Tuǒ (Appropriate)

E. 牵 5. Míng (Swear)

F. 妥 6. Qiān (Lead)

#142.

A. 渣 1. Zhā (Dregs)

B. 粭 2. Háng (Boat)

C. 凉 3. Huō (Hoeing)

D. 丧 4. Sāng (Funeral)

E. 娴 5. Xián (Refined)

F. 航 6. Liàng (Cool)

#143.

A. 怒 1. Qiāng (Ask)

B. 将 2. Nù (Angry)

C. 由 3. Zhǐ (Toe)

D. 趾 4. Kuài (A surname)

E. 郤 5. Xì (Red)

F. 赩 6. Yóu (Cause)

#144.

A. 孝 1. Huài (Bad)

B. 凑 2. Chá (Tea plant)

C. 馕 3. Náng (A kind of crusty pancake)

D. 矿 4. Còu (Happen by chance)

E. 坏 5. Xiào (Filial piety)

F. 茶 6. Kuàng (Ore deposit)

#145.

A. 隉 1. Lì (Encourage)

B. 舆 2. Găn (Catch up with)

C. 怜 3. Yú (Public)

D. 户 4. Hù (One-paneled door)

E. 励 5. Lián (Feel tender toward)

F. 赶 6. Niè (Uneasy)

#146.

A. 丱 1. Gòu (Meet)

B. 熏 2. Xūn (Smoke)

C. 恶 3. Tí (Raise)

D. 爱 4. Ài (Love)

E. 觏 5. Kuàng (Hair style)

F. 提 6. È (Evil)

#147.

A. 波 1. Dāng (Crotch)

B. 戟 2. Zhūn (Grave)

C. 氹 3. Rǔ (Disgrace)

D. 辱 4. Bō (Wave)

E. 窀 5. Jǐ (Halberd)

F. 裆 6. Dàng (Pool)

#148.

A. 瓿 1. Jiǎ (The first of the ten Heavenly Stems)

B. 戋 2. Xián (Epilepsy)

C. 痫 3. Jiān (Small)

D. 碗 4. Yǐ (Used at the end of a sentence (like 了))

E. 甲 5. Wǎn (Bowl)

F. 矣 6. Bù (Vase)

#149.

A. 彤 1. Tóng (Red)

B. 漏 2. Lòu (Leak)

C. 弨 3. Bēi (Carry on the back)

D. 背 4. Chún (Quail)

E. 沮 5. Jù (Moist)

F. 鹑 6. Chāo (Slack)

#150.

A. 皎 1. Yāo (Waist)

B. 阻 2. Chūn (Spring)

C. 畏 3. Wèi (Fear)

D. 腰 4. Zǔ (Block)

E. 绥 5. Jiǎo (Clear and bright)

F. 春 6. Suí (Peaceful)

ANSWERS (1-150)

#1.	F. Lǐn	D. Xì	B. Bó	#76.	F. Yā	D. Fú	B. Zhōng
A. Gōng		E. Zhōu	C. Jiāng	A. Guǎ		E. Yī	C. Yóu
B. Láng	#20.	F. Suǒ	D. Jiàn	B. Wěi	#95.	F. Xīng	D. Zhēng
C. Zhèng	A. Fén		E. Shēng	C. Miè	A. Qī		E. Kuài
D. Líng	B. Gāo	#39.	F. Rù	D. Yān	B. Xī	#114.	F. Rú
E. Yàng	C. Hēng	A. Yào		E. Nì	C. Qū	A. Hēng	
F. Qiāng	D. Biào	B. Liè	#58.	F. Yǎo	D. Jiāng	B. È	#133.
	E. Hú	C. Méi	A. gé		E. Qiǎ	C. Mí	A. Lián
#2.	F. Hán	D. Róu	B. Tài	#77.	F. Hàng	D. Tíng	B. Shú
A. Liáo		E. Zī	C. Shāo	A. Jì		E. Xū	C. Tīng
B. Yé	#21.	F. Qí	D. Pèi	B. Yì	#96.	F. Huī	D. Lán
C. Shēn	A. Liè		E. Jì	C. Pái	A. Jiè		E. Zhēn
D. Xiān	B. Zhì	#40.	F. Lòu	D. Yé	B. Bīn	#115.	F. Yā
E. Yòu	C. Lǐ	A. Chuāi		E. Zhì	C. Jiàng	A. Shī	
F. Táo	D. Kūn	B. Jì	#59.	F. Zhēng	D. Bǎn	B. Jìng	#134.
	E. Liáo	C. Nüè	A. Chóu		E. Din	C. Fén	A. Jǐn
#3.	F. Liú	D. Ruǎn	B. Qué	#78.	F. Chì	D. Jìn	B. Wāi
A. Kū		E. Yáo	C. Zhǎ	A. Shàng		E. Kūn	C. Zhuǎng
B. Fén	#22.	F. Xùn	D. Zhēng	B. Wēn	#97.	F. Hěn	D. Jiàn
C. Jǔ	A. Dài		E. Tóng	C. Huī	A. Qì		E. Lún
D. Zhūn	B. Xì	#41.	F. Duò	D. Yáo	B. Dàn	#116.	F. Nǎo
E. Xīng	C. Zhèng	A. Gū		E. Diū	C. Yù	A. Tùn	
F. Chǔn	D. Gān	B. Jià	#60.	F. Fén	D. Liào	B. Pàn	#135.
	E. Piān	C. Fù	A. Kē		E. Què	C. Suǒ	A. Shì
#4.	F. Mì	D. Míng	B. Nà	#79.	F. Gāo	D. Lì	B. Zhàn
A. Sà		E. Mì	C. Qiān	A. Qiàng		E. Qiān	C. Xiè
B. Jià	#23.	F. Jiù	D. Liáng	B. Hóng	#98.	F. Ēi	D. Ruǎn
C. Ào	A. Sháo		E. Jiǒng	C. Lù	A. Xī		E. Dàn
D. Kēng	B. Qí	#42.	F. Gē	D. Capture	B. Xiāng	#117.	F. Huì
E. Dàn	C. Jū	A. Cí		E. Tā	C. Méi	A. Bù	
F. Tóng	D. Bǎn	B. Cǎn	#61.	F. Xīn	D. Páng	B. Sān	#136.

	E. Yīng	C. Tóng	A. Kè		E. Luǎn	C. Dǔ	A. Yāo
#5.	F. Méng	D. Guān	B. Cóng	#80.	F. Guān	D. Lǐ	B. Dí
A. Pì		E. Tè	C. Lún	A. Tíng		E. Yāo	C. Qiān
B. Zhǎn	#24.	F. Píng	D. Dàng	B. Jiǒng	#99.	F. Zhào	D. Lín
C. Bì	A. Hòu		E. Huǎng	C. Yàn	A. Háng		E. Bà
D. Pǔ	B. Jiàn	#43.	F. Má	D. Nì	B. Shú	#118.	F. Yāng
E. Jìn	C. Wò	A. Gě		E. Nòng	C. Suí	A. Hái	
F. Zhēng	D. Zhōng	B. Sì	#62.	F. Mù	D. Bì	B. Fú	#137.
	E. Cǎi	C. Yìn	A. Gū		E. Qióng	C. Jū	A. Láng
#6.	F. Fěi	D. Gǔ	B. Jiē	#81.	F. Bàn	D. Jià	B. Kǎo
A. Tíng		E. Gěn	C. Hú	A. Míng		E. Xiàng	C. Fù
B. Yōng	#25.	F. Xún	D. Yùn	B. Lì	#100.	F. Xù	D. Shǔ
C. Zào	A. Gōng		E. Ōu	C. Jū	A. Yàn		E. Lún
D. Zā	B. Sǔn	#44.	F. Xiù	D. Yù	B. Qiú	#119.	F. Náng
E. Gǔ	C. Yā	A. Méi		E. Rǔ	C. Zhòu	A. Ruì	
F. Liú	D. Què	B. Fàn	#63.	F. Má	D. Jī	B. Zhào	#138.
	E. Gōng	C. Pù	A. Jiào		E. Shì	C. Lán	A. Huá
#7.	F. Tǎn	D. Chǎn	B. Fěi	#82.	F. Niáng	D. Bà	B. Xiāng
A. Sù		E. Tuó	C. Cù	A. Rèn		E. Yùn	C. Kē
B. Xún	#26.	F. Píng	D. Bì	B. Kuò	#101.	F. Zhì	D. Sǔn
C. Yún	A. Xùn		E. Tā	C. Méng	A. Biāo		E. Shè
D. Luō	B. Jǔ	#45.	F. Dīng	D. Zhá	B. Chuàn	#120.	F. Biān
E. Bīn	C. Chéng	A. Mà		E. Xiàn	C. Fèi	A. Yán	
F. Cī	D. Dìng	B. Lì	#64.	F. Yě	D. Chī	B. Jì	#139.
	E. Xiāo	C. Liú	A. Tī		E. Dān	C. Jiào	A. Shào
#8.	F. Tuǐ	D. Yìn	B. Hén	#83.	F. Qī	D. Náo	B. Wēn
A. È		E. Rèn	C. Mí	A. Jiān		E. Tuó	C. Kè
B. Nì	#27.	F. Sǎn	D. Yì	B. Biān	#102.	F. Xìng	D. Qiě
C. Guā	A. Jiǔ		E. Wǎng	C. Bèi	A. Qín		E. Shǐ
D. Liú	B. Jì	#46.	F. Jiàng	D. Jué	B. Nì	#121.	F. Juān
E. Cháo	C. Guǒ	A. Sǐ		E. Gé	C. Zuò	A. Mù	

F. Zǎo	D. Běn	B. Yāo	#65.	F. Nà	D. Zhuǎng	B. Pō	#140.
	E. Bèi	C. Cú	A. Fáng		E. Lián	C. Cuō	A. Zhān
#9.	F. Qīng	D. Yì	B. Zhá	#84.	F. Fàn	D. Nà	B. Méi
A. Làn		E. Chéng	C. Xī	A. Zhèn		E. Ruò	C. Fáng
B. Gàn	#28.	F. Fěi	D. Chàn	B. Shèn	#103.	F. Áo	D. Miǎn
C. Yún	A. Zhuàn		E. Shè	C. Xún	A. Gǔ		E. Jiāng
D. Shé	B. Qiān	#47.	F. Nián	D. Bā	B. Liáo	#122.	F. Tī
E. Shāo	C. Lì	A. Xī		E. Xū	C. Piān	A. Yì	
F. Ēi	D. Jié	B. Sōu	#66.	F. Lú	D. Juàn	B. Bǐ	#141.
	E. Fàn	C. Yán	A. Ruǎn		E. Jiāo	C. Yàn	A. Gāo
#10.	F. Fú	D. Diū	B. Shì	#85.	F. Shǐ	D. Nòu	B. Xiè
A. Má		E. Jiāo	C. Zhuàn	A. Zhuàn		E. Bǐng	C. Míng
B. Sǐ	#29.	F. Xī	D. Yù	B. Liáo	#104.	F. Zuǒ	D. Zhé
C. Hǎi	A. Zhē		E. Tán	C. Gǔ	A. Fēi		E. Qiān
D. Qǔ	B. Yūn	#48.	F. Sì	D. Wén	B. Tiè	#123.	F. Tuǒ
E. Zhǔ	C. Bìng	A. Běi		E. Dài	C. Gòu	A. Shuāng	
F. Shǎng	D. Shā	B. Ruò	#67.	F. Lún	D. Mèi	B. Qī	#142.
	E. Chén	C. Jīng	A. Gǒu		E. Kuí	C. Xū	A. Zhā
#11.	F. Líng	D. Xiáo	B. Xī	#86.	F. Jiào	D. Jù	B. Huō
A. Shē		E. Qiáng	C. Jū	A. Rě		E. Bǐng	C. Liàng
B. Huò	#30.	F. Jià	D. Shèng	B. Máng	#105.	F. Shāo	D. Sāng
C. Pí	A. Bāo		E. Gǔ	C. Suàn	A. Wǔ		E. Xián
D. Yú	B. Jiào	#49.	F. Wū	D. Jiù	B. Tuó	#124.	F. Háng
E. Sù	C. Xī	A. Zhà		E. Fèi	C. Shì	A. Cháng	
F. Xì	D. Piào	B. Wèi	#68.	F. Hū	D. Bó	B. Jué	#143.
	E. Nài	C. Máng	A. Tū		E. Rán	C. Bì	A. Nù
#12.	F. Zhān	D. Jiè	B. Guǎ	#87.	F. Pǎng	D. Lǐ	B. Qiāng
A. Xiào		E. Hún	C. Qié	A. Pǐ		E. Fēi	C. Yóu
B. Tū	#31.	F. Zhēng	D. Ěr	B. Jìshēng	#106.	F. Lán	D. Zhǐ
C. Yí	A. Wěi		E. Zhī	C. Lú	A. Tā		E. Kuài
D. Guī	B. Shàn	#50.	F. Tíng	D. Wān	B. Jí	#125.	F. Xì
E. Táo	C. Gǎi	A. Zhí		E. Shòu	C. Jiàng	A. Xiá	
F. Xiān	D. Fēi	B. Dùn	#69.	F. Yā	D. Liáng	B. Dài	#144.

	E. Kū	C. Yí	A. Lì		E. Wā	C. Dí	A. Xiào
#13.	F. Jiàng	D. Hún	B. Běi	#88.	F. Yǔ	D. Lǔ	B. Còu
A. Suān		E. Fàn	C. Kē	A. Dí		E. Liàng	C. Náng
B. Qiǎo	#32.	F. Hù	D. Zhēng	B. Wāng	#107.	F. Jūn	D. Kuàng
C. Pán	A. Sān		E. Qióng	C. Pēng	A. Biǎo		E. Huài
D. Háo	B. Shè	#51.	F. Là	D. Dèng	B. Yǎ	#126.	F. Chá
E. Shí	C. Dàng	A. Qǔ		E. Zhàn	C. Cè	A. Zài	
F. Xī	D. Guì	B. Tāng	#70.	F. Bǎn	D. Zhèn	B. Huī	#145.
	E. Kuài	C. Yú	A. Lái		E. Yūn	C. Jīn	A. Niè
#14.	F. Dǔ	D. Duì	B. Táo	#89.	F. Tuǒ	D. Tóng	B. Yú
A. Dǒu		E. Gǒu	C. Xīn	A. Wǎng		E. Zhōu	C. Lián
B. Bǎ	#33.	F. Kū	D. Huī	B. Yǐ	#108.	F. Míng	D. Hù
C. Sù	A. Biāo		E. Diǎn	C. Jiè	A. Lè		E. Lì
D. Cè	B. Xíng	#52.	F. Cè	D. Yàn	B. Fù	#127.	F. Gǎn
E. Gá	C. Liú	A. Jí		E. Lián	C. Mò	A. Èr	
F. Huò	D. Gān	B. Shèng	#71.	F. Bāo	D. Dǒu	B. Liáo	#146.
	E. Chū	C. Áo	A. Qiǎ		E. Diāo	C. Mì	A. Kuàng
#15.	F. Ròu	D. Chái	B. Fáng	#90.	F. Yù	D. Sì	B. Xūn
A. Chǎ		E. Shà	C. Dōng	A. Cī		E. Mó	C. È
B. Shì	#34.	F. Bā	D. Lǒu	B. Xián	#109.	F. Miù	D. Ài
C. Fēi	A. Dān		E. Kěn	C. Yě	A. Fù		E. Gòu
D. Bēi	B. Ào	#53.	F. Bēi	D. Cǐ	B. Tǎ	#128.	F. Tí
E. Hé	C. Liú	A. Yǔn		E. Guī	C. Zhòu	A. Pō	
F. Guǐ	D. Qī	B. Biàn	#72.	F. Chā	D. Wù	B. Hé	#147.
	E. Dā	C. Màn	A. Shòu		E. Zhá	C. Rèn	A. Bō
#16.	F. Huái	D. Hóu	B. Tì	#91.	F. Yīn	D. Rǎn	B. Jǐ
A. Fú		E. Jì	C. Zhòng	A. Biàn		E. Fù	C. Dàng
B. Yù	#35.	F. Chú	D. Hè	B. Qiān	#110.	F. Cū	D. Rǔ
C. Zā	A. Jì		E. Wǎn	C. Qī	A. Lěi		E. Zhūn
D. Lú	B. Kē	#54.	F. Yīng	D. Běi	B. Qiān	#129.	F. Dāng
E. Shú	C. Qián	A. Tà		E. Xún	C. Pēng	A. Dàng	
F. Diǎn	D. Qì	B. Zhú	#73.	F. Dā	D. Dì	B. Qiān	#148.
	E. Sǔn	C. Nài	A. Kòng		E. Qīng	C. Zài	A. Bù
#17.	F. Jué	D. Fēn	B. Yǐ	#92.	F. Yíng	D. Gū	B. Jiān
A. Qíng		E. Zhàn	C. Liè	A. Suān		E. Cāi	C. Xián

B. Qiǎo	#36.	F. Jì	D. Huán	B. Zāo	#111.	F. Xuàn	D. Wǎn
C. Hán	A. Sù		E. Xíng	C. Dàn	A. Tí		E. Jiǎ
D. Liú	B. Tái	#55.	F. Huá	D. Chī	B. Qìng	#130.	F. Yǐ
E. Lí	C. Líng	A. Chè		E. Bāo	C. Qián	A. Gǒu	
F. Jiàng	D. Lǎn	B. Líng	#74.	F. Mǐn	D. Luó	B. Tǎn	#149.
	E. Huī	C. Yóu	A. Wén		E. Lǐn	C. Dìng	A. Tóng
#18.	F. Kuān	D. Qiú	B. Xī	#93.	F. Sān	D. Yuán	B. Lòu
A. Nüè		E. Yōu	C. Shěn	A. Chā		E. Táng	C. Chāo
B. Cǎn	#37.	F. Gū	D. Mì	B. Jì	#112.	F. Huī	D. Bēi
C. Suí	A. Fán		E. Tè	C. Dàn	A. Zhǎn		E. Jù
D. Chóu	B. Qǔ	#56.	F. Guà	D. Dǒu	B. Jìng	#131.	F. Chún
E. Kū	C. Yù	A. Yìn		E. Jié	C. Huà	A. Xiáng	
F. Tuì	D. Shì	B. Zhā	#75.	F. Qí	D. Hé	B. Shāng	#150.
	E. Kuí	C. Lǒng	A. Yù		E. Pó	C. Dàng	A. Jiǎo
#19.	F. Xiào	D. Sān	B. Jǔ	#94.	F. Tīng	D. Zhǔ	B. Zǔ
A. Tuǒ		E. Chǎo	C. Zhī	A. Gāng		E. Hǎo	C. Wèi
B. Běi	#38.	F. Wú	D. Tè	B. Jiào	#113.	F. Lóu	D. Yāo
C. Kuàng	A. Sī		E. Xiè	C. Hū	A. Xiū		E. Suí
D. Jié	B. Chā	#57.	F. Piāo	D. Fén	B. Chù	#132.	F. Chūn
E. Gān	C. Nú	A. Huà		E. Hēng	C. Lóng	A. Yáo	

Milton Keynes UK
Ingram Content Group UK Ltd.
UKHW051113211123
432908UK00032B/2208